The Gown Opens in the Front

A Journal for Cancer Patients

Published by:
Whitehall Publishing.
PO Box 548
Yellville, AR 72687
www.whitehallpublishing.com
E-mail info@whitehallpublishing.com

Wheresmyboob.com
PO Box 122322
Covington, Kentucky 41012-2322

Cover Design By:
Ascender Graphix,
http://www.ascendergraphix.com

ISBN# 978-1-935122-21-0
Retail Price $12.99
Printed in the United State of America.

Dear Friend,

This journal is a "prompted" journal that I designed. It was inspired by several of my favorite books and quotes, as well as by my own writing. I hope that this will help you find yourself during your battle and recovery from cancer.

This journal is meant to be for self expression and for play. You can start at page one and work your way through, or you can fill out whichever page you feel like writing in for the day. Feel free to let your imagination go. There are many blank pages for drawing and journaling as well.

There will be some days that you are feisty, some days that you are sad, some days that you feel ecstatic, and some bad days, too. Keeping track of them will help you to realize how much you are growing and healing as you recover from cancer.

I suggest that you record the date and time of each journal entry, because that will help you keep track of your progress as well.

Please remember that I'm not a trained professional, unless you count fighting cancer for 2 years, surviving two rounds of chemo, radiation, multiple surgeries and being prescribed just about every cancer related drug on the market as training! This journal is a reflection of what my heart is telling me, not a result of education. If you have any questions about your treatment, you should consult your physician right away.

I am praying for you and hoping that your recovery is speedy and miraculous. You are not alone.

Love,

Rachael Logsdon

My Medical Information

This is a great page to make a copy of and keep on hand for hospitalizations and doctors' appointments. Sometimes you just get tired of telling people the same things over and over again! Plus, it helps to keep this updated if you are too sick to remember all of the details!

Date of Birth: _____

Medication Name	Dosage	How many times a day

Allergies to Medications: yes   no - (if yes, list those drugs below)

Surgeries:

Date:	Type of Surgery	Any Complications?

Chemotherapy:

Name of Chemo:	Dosage:	Date of Last Chemo:

Table of Contents

My Journal

Diagnosis

Diagnosis

From Rachael's Journal

6-17-2005 10:00am - I still can't believe that I have cancer. Well, sometimes I believe it, and other times I don't. I feel unclean, like I have a parasite or something. Every time I'm in the shower, I want to scrub my boob really hard.

I have too many questions!

What will I look like bald?

What if I deserve this?

What if the cancer has spread to other areas of my body?

What if my docs are just acting optimistic to make me feel less afraid and they know that I am going to die?

What if I have an allergic reaction to chemo, and no one is there to help me?

Is there someone out there with a voodoo doll?

Now What?

Ok, so you were diagnosed with cancer, now what?

Here are some statistics from the American Cancer Society from 2009.

"Death rates from breast cancer have been declining since about 1990, with larger decreases in women younger than 50. These decreases are believed to be the result of earlier detection through screening and increased awareness, as well as improved treatment.

At this time there are over 2.5 million breast cancer survivors in the United States. (This includes women still being treated and those who have completed treatment.)" *That number represents more people than the combined populations of Dallas Texas, Miami Florida and San Francisco, California.* Now that you have some real numbers and some real perspective...

Now that I know that, I feel

_____

_____

_____

_____

_____

_____

_____

_____

_____

Diagnosis

I put together some quotes from people who have been where you are today and have not JUST survived, they have thrived. I want these quotes to be with you throughout your journey to support and inspire you when you need it! By the way, I left room at the bottom of this page for YOUR quote!

"Cancer is a word, not a sentence." **John Diamond**

"If children have the ability to ignore all odds and percentages, then maybe we can all learn from them. When you think about it, what other choice is there but to hope? We have two options, medically and emotionally: give up, or Fight Like Hell." **Lance Armstrong**

"My cancer scare changed my life. I'm grateful for every new, healthy day I have. It has helped me prioritize my life." **Olivia Newton John**

"It has been an extraordinary experience and, in many ways, extremely positive." **Marianne Faithful** On her successful recovery from breast cancer.

"Well even before she was diagnosed with the cancer, I would have said that she was a lot tougher than me and most guys would probably say that about their wives and it's probably true in most cases." **Brett Favre**

Your Quote:_____

_____

_____

Date: _____

Uh Oh.

_____

_____

_____

_____

I've been diagnosed with cancer.

My biopsy date was: _____

I feel _____

_____

_____

_____

_____

_____

_____

_____

_____

_____

_____

_____

_____

_____

_____

Diagnosis

I wonder if _____

_____

_____

_____

_____

_____

_____

_____

_____

_____

_____

_____

_____

_____

_____

_____

_____

_____

_____

_____

I met my oncologist today.

He/she is: _____

_____

_____

_____

_____

_____

_____

_____

_____

_____

_____

_____

I feel _____ about having this person save my life.

_____

_____

_____

_____

_____

_____

_____

_____

Diagnosis

My cancer is staged at _____

This means _____

_____

_____

_____

_____

_____

_____

_____

_____

_____

I have more tests to do, but so far, my treatment plan is to

_____

_____

_____

_____

_____

_____

_____

This is how I really feel about this whole situation right now

_____

_____

_____

_____

_____

_____

_____

_____

_____

_____

_____

_____

_____

_____

_____

_____

_____

_____

_____

_____

_____

Diagnosis

Questions about my diagnosis:

_____

_____

_____

_____

_____

_____

_____

_____

_____

_____

_____

_____

_____

_____

_____

_____

_____

_____

_____

"When you come to the end of your rope,
tie a knot and hang on."
Franklin D. Roosevelt

My Thoughts

_____

_____

_____

_____

_____

_____

_____

_____

_____

_____

_____

_____

_____

_____

_____

_____

_____

_____

_____

_____

_____

Diagnosis

My Thoughts

_____

_____

_____

_____

_____

_____

_____

_____

_____

_____

_____

_____

_____

_____

_____

_____

_____

_____

_____

_____

_____

_____

You've had a lot to digest since you got your diagnosis. I want to share with you some helpful quotes from people who have been right here themselves and won their battle! Let their words help inspire you to win your battle too.

"It is a simple thing to be healed of cancer.
It is the body that does the work, not my head.
I only furnish it with the tools needed to obtain good health. ...
My journey was interesting and I still claim that cancer
was the best thing that ever happened to me.
It woke me up out of my passivity and gave me focus and energy
and an awareness of my character. ... Cancer good or bad it is,
as all of life, in how you look at it.
For me it was very good and taught me much about myself.
After all, it matters to have an end to journey towards,
but it is the journey that matters in the end. ...
I always say it is about the journey not the cancer."
Dennis Robinson, PhD, and cancer survivor

"We are continually faced with great opportunities
which are brilliantly disguised as unsolvable problems."
Margaret Mead

"Always laugh when you can, it is cheap medicine.
Merriment - it is the sunny side of existence."
Lord Bryon

Diagnosis

My Thoughts

_____

_____

_____

_____

_____

_____

_____

_____

_____

_____

_____

_____

_____

_____

_____

_____

_____

_____

_____

_____

_____

_____

_____

My Thoughts

_____
_____
_____
_____
_____
_____
_____
_____
_____
_____
_____
_____
_____
_____
_____
_____
_____
_____
_____
_____
_____
_____

Diagnosis - Important Terms

Some Words you Will Need to Know...

Before you begin treatment, it is helpful to familiarize yourself with some terminology. Here are some words that you should probably be familiar with. Not only should you know what these words mean, but how they will play a part in your life in the weeks to come. Most of these words can be found on the American Cancer Society's website...

Anemia - (uh-neem-ee-uh): low red blood cell count.

Biopsy - (by-op-see): the removal of a sample of tissue to see whether cancer cells are present. There are several kinds of biopsies. In some, a very thin needle is used to draw fluid and cells from a lump. Tumor markers - substance produced by cancer cells and sometimes normal cells. They are not very useful for cancer screening because other body tissues not related to a cancer can produce the substance, too. But tumor markers may be very useful in monitoring for response to treatment when a cancer is diagnosed or for a recurrence.

Chemotherapy - (key-mo-THER-uh-pee): treatment with drugs to destroy cancer cells. Chemotherapy is often used, either alone or with surgery or radiation, to treat cancer that has spread or come back (recurred), or when there is a strong chance that it could recur. Often called *chemo*.

Computed Tomography - (to-mahg-ruh-fee): an imaging test in which many x-rays are taken from different angles of a part of the body. These images are combined by a computer to make cross-sectional pictures of internal organs. Except for the injection of a dye (needed in some but not all cases), this is a painless procedure that can be done in an outpatient clinic. *It is often referred to as a "CT" or "CAT" scan.*

Genetic Testing - tests performed to see if a person has certain gene changes known to increase cancer risk.

Fatigue - (fuh-teeg): a common symptom during cancer treatment, a bone-weary exhaustion that doesn't get better with rest. For some, this can last for some time after treatment.

Immune system - the complex system by which the body resists infection by germs, such as bacteria or viruses, and rejects transplanted tissues or organs. The immune system may also help the body fight some cancers.

MRI - magnetic resonance imaging (MRI): a method of taking pictures of the inside of the body. Instead of using x-rays, MRI uses a powerful magnet to send radio waves through the body. The images appear on a computer screen as well as on film. Like x-rays, the procedure is physically painless, but some people may feel confined inside the MRI machine.

Neulasta® - is a white blood cell booster to help support your natural defenses and help reduce the risk of infection in patients with some tumors receiving strong chemotherapy.

PET Scan - positron emission tomography (PET): (pahs-uh-trahn ee-mish-uhn tom-**ahg**-ruh-fee): a PET scan creates an image of the body (or of biochemical events) after the injection of a very low dose of a radioactive form of a substance such as glucose (sugar). The scan computes the rate at which the tumor is using the sugar. In general, high-grade tumors use more sugar than normal and low-grade tumors use less.

Portacath - A portacath is a device that is placed under your skin. It is used to inject chemo drugs and obtain blood. With a portacath, your veins are no longer inserted with needles. This will eliminate an immense amount of strain on your veins.

Radiation Therapy - treatment with high-energy rays (such as x-rays) to kill cancer cells and shrink tumors. The radiation may come from outside the body (external radiation) or from radioactive materials placed directly in the tumor (brachytherapy or internal radiation).

Knowing these words will help to alleviate some of your fears.

Diagnosis - Dealing with Fear

Fear

One of the worst parts of dealing with cancer is dealing with the fear.

What am I afraid of?

_____

_____

_____

_____

_____

_____

_____

_____

_____

_____

_____

_____

_____

_____

_____

_____

_____

_____

_____

How do you handle the fear?

Do you fret and worry?

Do you push it away?

Do you have healthy ways to face it?

If you are having trouble facing your fear, it may be time to talk to a professional. In the meantime, here is a list of possible things you can do when you are feeling overwhelmed and afraid.

Clean the house	Cook a meal for a loved one
Dance	Do laundry
Do some light yoga	Go for a walk
Go get a facial or pedicure	Go shopping
Go to a movie	Listen to music
List the things that make you happy	Paint
Play on Facebook®	Play a video game
Plant flowers	Practice deep breathing
Pray	Read a book
Read a magazine	Repeat a mantra
Take a hot bath or shower	Watch a movie with a loved one
Weed the garden	Write in your journal!

Diagnosis - Dealing with Fear

Feeling out of control is so awful. Fill out this list, you'll be surprised!

Things I CAN Control	Things I Can't Control

Here is my list that I wrote during my treatment.
I share it with you to help you expand your own list!

Rachael's List	
Things that _I CAN_ control	**Things that _I CAN'T_ control**
1. Quitting smoking,	1. I have cancer - (This is really worth two points, I think),
2. How I talk to people, and how I express my feelings,	2. Other peoples feelings/ reactions,
3. What time my appointments are, and whether or not I go to the appointments,	3. I need chemotherapy,
4. Who my doctors are,	4. This will have an effect on my personal relationships,
5. My nutrition,	
6. What I read and watch on TV,	
7. Whether or not I answer the phone,	
8. Who I talk to about my illness,	
9. What type of surgery I have,	
10. Who I ask for help.	

Diagnosis - Dealing with Fear

Which side of your list is longer? How do you feel about that?

_____

_____

_____

_____

_____

_____

_____

_____

_____

_____

_____

_____

_____

_____

_____

_____

_____

"Cancer is a disease where the patient can
contribute a great deal of help himself
if he or she can retain their morale and their hopes."
George Carman

Thoughts About Fear:

"Courage is doing what you're afraid to do.
There can be no courage unless you're scared."
Edward Vernon Rickenbacker

What are you most afraid of?

_____

_____

_____

_____

_____

_____

_____

_____

_____

_____

_____

_____

_____

_____

_____

_____

_____

Diagnosis - Dealing with Fear

How do you think your life and your treatment would change if you could work through your fear and let it go?

_____

_____

_____

_____

_____

_____

_____

_____

_____

_____

_____

_____

_____

_____

_____

"Become a possibilitarian.
No matter how dark things seem to be or actually are,
raise your sights and see possibilities -
always see them,
for they're always there."
Norman Vincent Peale

Treatment

Treatment - Portacath

Getting a Portacath

So your portacath/central line is new. How do you feel when you look at it?

_____

_____

_____

_____

_____

_____

_____

_____

_____

_____

_____

_____

_____

_____

_____

Have you shown it to anyone?

_____

_____

_____

_____

_____

What did you think the first time you heard about getting a portacath?

_____

_____

_____

_____

_____

_____

_____

_____

_____

_____

_____

_____

_____

_____

_____

_____

_____

"I feel more inspired than ever,
and think that I will finally achieve
what I have long been wishing for:
a balance of work and privacy - a harmony."
Kylie Minogue, On getting through her battle against cancer.

Treatment - Chemotherapy

From Rachael's Journal

4-14-2006 - People ask me about chemotherapy all the time, now that I am finished with it. They say they were afraid to ask me what I was going through. Why? I always wonder. Why are people so afraid to ask questions about cancer, or to think about it?

Chemotherapy is do-able. It is not impossible and there is no shame in it. In fact, honor yourself for being so brave!!!

Has your doctor explained the side effects of your particular chemotherapy?

_____

_____

_____

_____

_____

_____

_____

What medications will you be getting along with your chemo?

_____

_____

_____

_____

_____

_____

_____

_____

Hair Loss

How do you feel about hair loss?

_____

_____

_____

_____

_____

_____

_____

_____

Are you going to get a wig?

What do you think it will look like?

_____

_____

_____

_____

_____

_____

_____

_____

_____

_____

29

Wig fun!

Color the wigs different colors and place them over your photo!

place your photo here...

Getting ready

Are you ready for your first chemo?

_____

_____

_____

_____

_____

_____

_____

_____

_____

_____

Here are some things that you may want to have ready and waiting for you at home before you go to your first chemo treatment to make you feel more comfy during your chemo...

Baby Powder or body powder

Butterscotch candies

Good hand/foot moisturizer

Soft, comfortable pajamas

Someone to walk the dog

Yogurt

Books on CD or iTunes

Chapstick

Raspberry Sherbet

Soft, fuzzy Socks

Tissues

TIP: Numbing medicine for your port (ask your oncologist to prescribe this to you).

Treatment - Chemotherapy

Sometimes it's nice to have a list of things to do before your chemo to take your mind off of things.

Here are some things you can do to make your first chemo more comfortable:

¥ Drink LOTS of water the day before,

¥ Go get a massage, Reiki, Shi Gong or healing touch therapy 1-3 days ahead of time,

¥ Clean the toilets (you might not throw up, but better safe than sorry!),

¥ Arrange to have some prepared meals for the next few days,

¥ Stock up on soup,

¥ Make sure there are plenty of ice cubes in the freezer,

¥ Put clean sheets on the bed and sprinkle some baby powder on them,

¥ Catch up on laundry and make sure there are clean towels in the bathroom.

Your first chemo... How do you feel?

_____

_____

_____

Day 1

_____

_____

_____

Day 2

_____

_____

_____

Day 3

_____

_____

_____

Day 4

_____

_____

_____

Day 5

_____

_____

_____

Treatment - Chemotherapy

Day 6

_____

_____

_____

Day 7

_____

_____

_____

Day 8

_____

_____

_____

Day 9

_____

_____

_____

Day 10

_____

_____

_____

What can you do to help yourself be more comfortable for next time?

_____

_____

_____

_____

I thought chemo was going to be

_____

_____

_____

_____

_____

_____

_____

_____

Now I know that chemo is

_____

_____

_____

_____

_____

_____

_____

_____

I feel gross

_____

_____

_____

_____

Treatment-Chemotherapy

I think that chemo is

_____

_____

_____

_____

_____

_____

_____

_____

_____

_____

_____

_____

_____

_____

_____

_____

_____

_____

_____

_____

_____

Hair Loss

Today, my hair started to come out.

Well, that was fast...

I felt

_____
_____
_____
_____
_____
_____
_____
_____

I reacted by

_____
_____
_____
_____
_____
_____
_____
_____
_____
_____
_____
_____
_____

Treatment - Chemotherapy Side Effects

I am afraid

_____

_____

_____

_____

_____

_____

_____

_____

I feel

_____

_____

_____

_____

_____

_____

_____

_____

_____

_____

I would like to

_____

_____

_____

_____

_____

_____

_____

_____

I think that hair loss is

_____

_____

_____

_____

_____

_____

_____

_____

Treatment - Chemotherapy Side Effects

I can't sleep

_____

_____

_____

_____

_____

_____

_____

_____

_____

_____

_____

_____

_____

_____

_____

_____

_____

_____

_____

_____

Pain

Pain is a scary thing to deal with. Sometimes, it's a result of healing. Other times, it's a result of something breaking apart.

What hurts?

_____

_____

_____

_____

_____

What can you do to relieve the pain?

_____

_____

_____

_____

_____

_____

_____

Pain is there for a reason. It is an indicator.
What is your pain telling you?

_____

_____

_____

_____

Treatment - Chemotherapy Side Effects

Thoughts about pain:

_____

_____

_____

_____

_____

_____

_____

_____

_____

_____

_____

_____

_____

_____

_____

_____

_____

_____

_____

_____

_____

Chemobrain

Chemobrain isn't so bad. Sometimes, it's kind of pleasant.

Thoughts about chemo brain...

Are there any?

Do you even remember

what we are talking about?

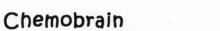

OKAY, I FOUND MY PURSE. WHERE THE HELL ARE MY KEYS?

_____

_____

_____

_____

_____

_____

_____

_____

_____

_____

_____

_____

_____

_____

_____

Vivid Dreams

Dreams can tell us so many things. Sometimes the medications that accompany chemotherapy can cause nightmares. Writing down the dreams that you have can give them less power. They can also help you to understand if the dream has special meaning for you.

Dream Journaling

Last night, I dreamed	What did it mean?	What can I tell myself?

Last night, I dreamed	What did it mean?	What can I tell myself?

Fatigue

Are you really wanting to write? If not, take a nap! If so, how are you today?

_____

_____

_____

_____

_____

_____

_____

_____

_____

_____

_____

_____

What, is it noon already?

_____

_____

_____

_____

_____

_____

_____

_____

Nausea

Have you found a nausea medication that makes you more comfortable? Don't give up, there are lots of them out there!

_____

_____

_____

_____

_____

_____

_____

_____

Have you tried sucking on ice cubes or crushed ice? It doesn't fix the nausea, but it can be comforting. It can help to soothe you if your mouth gets sore too.

_____

_____

_____

_____

_____

_____

_____

_____

_____

Treatment - Chemotherapy Side Effects

Thoughts about nausea:

_____

_____

_____

_____

_____

_____

_____

_____

_____

_____

_____

_____

_____

_____

_____

_____

_____

_____

_____

_____

_____

_____

Menopause

How long has it been since you've had a period?

_____

_____

_____

Are you having hot flashes? If you are, what is that like?

_____

_____

_____

_____

_____

_____

_____

_____

_____

_____

_____

_____

_____

Chemotherapy

The second type of chemotherapy usually has different types of sides effects than the first chemo. There is no one type of chemo that is "easier" than another. They are all tough in their own way.

Has your doctor explained the side effects of your particular chemotherapy?

_____
_____
_____
_____
_____
_____
_____

What medications will you be getting along with your chemo?

_____
_____
_____
_____
_____
_____
_____
_____

You'll still have a couple months of baldness. How do you feel about it now that you are used to dealing with it?

_____

_____

_____

_____

_____

_____

_____

Your first new chemo... How do you feel?

_____

_____

_____

_____

_____

_____

_____

_____

_____

_____

_____

_____

_____

I Don't want to go tomorrow

Treatment - Chemotherapy Side Effects

How do you feel?

Day 1

_____
_____
_____
_____

Day 2

_____
_____
_____
_____

Day 3

_____
_____
_____

Day 4

_____
_____
_____
_____

Day 5

_____
_____
_____
_____

Day 6

_____
_____
_____

Day 7

_____
_____
_____

Day 8

_____
_____
_____

Day 9

_____
_____
_____

Day 10

_____
_____
_____

What can you do to help yourself be more comfortable for next time?

_____
_____

Treatment - Chemotherapy Side Effects

Did you have any misconceptions about what this type of chemo would be like?

_____

_____

_____

_____

_____

_____

_____

Now that you know what it will be like, how do you feel?

_____

_____

_____

_____

_____

I am tired of feeling so gross.

_____

_____

_____

_____

_____

_____

Neuropathy

Some types of chemo cause neuropathy, which leads to a tingling/ numbness in the hands and feet. Sometimes it can be uncomfortable. One way to help with this is to wear soft, fitted gloves in the house, or to get a moist-heat heating pad. Another way to help with the discomfort is to use a hot water bottle. If neuropathy gets unbearable, contact your oncologist.

I feel

_____

_____

_____

_____

_____

_____

_____

_____

_____

_____

_____

_____

_____

Treatment - Chemotherapy Side Effects

From Rachael's Journal:

Journal Entry Aug 25, 2005 - When you have cancer, most of the time you are caught up in the momentum of events. Gotta' go to this doctor and that doctor. Gotta' get this test done and that test done. Most of the time you are so focused on events that you push the fact that you have a serious illness and are suffering out of your thoughts. Then little things happen to remind you. Losing your hair for the first time, dreams, a quiet moment, or a lull in the excitement. That's when it gets scary. That's also when you get closer to finding peace. I always sleep really well after a nervous breakdown in the shower.

Thoughts:

_____

_____

_____

_____

I Don't want to go tomorrow

_____

_____

_____

_____

_____

_____

_____

Pain

Do you have more or less pain than with your last type of chemo?
What hurts?

_____
_____
_____
_____
_____

What can you do to relieve the pain?

_____
_____
_____
_____

Thoughts about pain:

_____
_____
_____
_____
_____
_____
_____

Treatment - Chemotherapy Side Effects

Dream Journaling

Last night, I dreamed	What did it mean?	What can I tell myself?

Treatment - Chemotherapy Side Effects
Dream Journaling

Last night, I dreamed	What did it mean?	What can I tell myself?

Treatment - Chemotherapy Side Effects

Fatigue

How are you today?

_____

_____

_____

_____

_____

_____

_____

_____

_____

_____

_____

_____

_____

What, is it noon already?

_____

_____

_____

_____

_____

_____

_____

_____

_____

By now, you are probably an old hat at all of this, and you are into the routine. What things have you learned about what you can handle that you never would have dreamed possible?

_____

_____

_____

_____

_____

_____

_____

_____

_____

_____

_____

_____

_____

_____

_____

_____

_____

_____

Surgery

My doctor has recommended that I have surgery

_____

_____

_____

_____

_____

_____

We decided that I will

_____

_____

_____

_____

_____

My surgery will be

_____

_____

_____

_____

_____

_____

_____

"Optimism is the foundation of courage."
Nicholas Murray Butler

Surgery

Surgery

Many surgeons believe that their patients can hear them during the surgery. Lots of times, they will talk to you during the procedure if you ask them to. Ask your surgeon to talk to you before you wake up and say something like, "you will wake up relaxed and comfortable, with your loved ones all around you." You'll be surprised at the difference it makes in how easily you wake up afterwards!

I'm afraid to have an operation because

_____

_____

_____

_____

_____

_____

_____

_____

_____

_____

_____

_____

_____

_____

_____

_____

Here's what my body looks like now:

_____
_____
_____
_____
_____
_____
_____
_____

Here's what it will look like after surgery:

_____
_____
_____
_____
_____
_____
_____
_____
_____
_____
_____
_____

Surgery

Thoughts on surgery:

_____

_____

_____

_____

_____

_____

_____

_____

_____

"Every tomorrow has two handles.
We can take hold of it by the handle of anxiety,
or by the handle of faith."
Author Unknown

_____

_____

_____

_____

_____

_____

_____

_____

_____

Boob Jobs Fun?
Is it possible for reconstruction to be fun?
Planning for it can be!

Booby Shower

Here are some instructions on how to throw a "shower" for your new boobs!

1. Send out invitations using baby shower cards. (Just cross out "baby" and write "booby" or make your own cards),
2. Register at target, Walmart, Meijer, Dillards, wherever you want under a baby shower registry. Register for silk and flannel pajamas, comfy clothes, books, dvds, board games, whatever you think will help to make your recovery easy and fun,
3. Make up games, like word scrambles, pin the pasty on the booby, etc.,
4. Order a boob shaped cake for more fun, or you can make booby shaped cupcakes,
5. Order pizza,
6. Buy a piece of poster board and glue your favorite pictures in the center. At the party, have all of your friends sign it with a fun message. Ask the nurses to tape it to the wall so that it is the first thing you see when you wake up after surgery,
7. For more info on holding a booby shower, visit our website at www.wheresmyboob.com. You can order a booby shower kit, or find free game ideas at the website,
8. Sit back and wait for the party to happen!

Notes for my own New Booby Shower:

_____

_____

_____

_____

_____

Surgery

"A good laugh and a long sleep
are the best cures in the doctor's book."
Irish Proverb

My Booby Shower was

_____

_____

_____

_____

_____

_____

My Favorite Moment

_____

_____

_____

_____

_____

_____

Attendees at the party

_____

_____

_____

What I will remember most about the event

_____

_____

_____

_____

From Rachael's Journal

9-14-2005 Journal Entry - Today is the day before my surgery. This morning, I ran around like a freak, trying to make an appointment to have my boobs marked on for the TRAM procedure. I don't understand why they don't use permanent markers. They told me that I can't take a shower today or tomorrow, because the ink would wash off. I thought, okay, fine. But it is so humid outside that it has all rubbed off just from me sweating, getting in and out of the car and going to the house. GRRR. My belly is just one purple blob. I hope they write on me again tomorrow, cuz it makes me a little nervous to think of Dr . Sillins starting from scratch when I'm already under. I hope that doesn't happen, because I'd really like to be symmetrical when I wake up.

Am having nightmares that my plastic surgeon sucks out my tummy fat and injects all of it into my chin. Will leave a note on my chest before they put me under saying stay below the dotted line please.

Surgery

My surgery is tomorrow. I feel

_____

_____

_____

_____

_____

_____

I'm most afraid of

_____

_____

_____

_____

_____

_____

I'm most excited about

_____

_____

_____

_____

_____

"Every adversity, every failure, every heartache
carries with it the seed of an equal or greater benefit."
Napoleon Hill

Surgery

Recovering From Surgery

Ouch. I'm sore

_____

_____

_____

_____

_____

I think I am

_____

_____

_____

_____

_____

_____

I am most looking forward to

_____

_____

_____

_____

_____

_____

_____

_____

Surgery

Taking care of surgical wounds can be a little scary, but you can do it! Hint- maxi pads or preemie diapers are much more absorbent and cheaper than gauze. Just be sure to put a piece of gauze over the wound so that you know that the wound stays clean.

I have drains. Ewwww.

It's been_____days since my surgery. I feel

_____

_____

_____

_____

_____

_____

_____

_____

_____

I am most looking forward to

_____

_____

_____

_____

_____

_____

It's been _____ days since my surgery. I feel

_____

_____

_____

_____

_____

_____

_____

_____

_____

It's been _____ days since my surgery. I feel

_____

_____

_____

_____

_____

_____

_____

_____

_____

_____

_____

_____

Surgery

It's been _____ days since my surgery. I feel

_____

_____

_____

_____

_____

_____

I feel so much better today!

_____

_____

_____

_____

_____

_____

Today, my surgeon told me

_____

_____

_____

_____

_____

_____

Thoughts about surgery:

_____

_____

_____

_____

_____

What surprised me about my surgery

_____

_____

_____

_____

What I am most looking forward to now that the surgery is over

_____

_____

_____

_____

_____

_____

_____

_____

Surgery

Now that surgery is behind you, I wanted to give you a little pick-me-up with some quotes from people who have been there, done that!

"The most important thing in illness
is never to lose heart."
Nikolai Lenin

"Attitude is a little thing that makes a big difference."
Winston Churchill

"Some days there won't be a song in your heart.
Sing anyway."
Emory Austin

"The human spirit is stronger
than anything that can happen to it."
C.C. Scott

Radiation

Glossary for Radiation Treatments

Below is a glossary of terms from the American Cancer Society that you may find helpful. You can visit their website at: http://www.cancer.org.

accelerated radiation: radiation schedule in which the total dose is given over a shorter period of time. (Compare to hyperfractionated radiation.)

adjuvant therapy (add-joo-vunt): a treatment used in addition to the main (primary) therapy. Radiation therapy often is used as an adjuvant to surgery.

anti-emetic (an-tie-eh-MEH-tik): a drug to prevent or treat nausea or vomiting.

brachytherapy (brake-ee-THER-uh-pee): internal radiation treatment done by implanting radioactive material directly into the tumor or close to it. Also called internal radiation therapy.

centigray (cGy) (sent-uh-gray): the preferred measurement of the amount of radiation dose absorbed by the body (1 cGy = 1 rad).

conformal radiation therapy (con-for-mul ray-dee-A-shun): a newer type of radiation treatment that uses a special computer to help shape the beam of radiation to match the shape of the tumor and delivers the beam from different directions. This reduces the amount of exposure to nearby healthy tissues.

dietitian (also registered dietitian): a health professional who plans well-balanced diet programs, including special diets to meet needs of people with various medical conditions.

dosimetrist (doe-sim-uh-trist):: a person who plans and calculates the proper radiation dose for treatment.

electron beam (ee-leck-tron): a stream of high-energy particles called electrons used to treat cancer.

external radiation: radiation therapy that uses a machine located outside of the body to aim high-energy rays at cancer cells.

fractionation (frack-shun-A-shun): dividing the total dose of radiation into smaller doses in order to reduce damage to healthy tissues.

gamma rays: high-energy rays that come from a radioactive source such as cobalt-60.

helical tomotherapy (he-lick-ul toe-mah-gruff-ee): a newer form of intensity modulated radiation therapy (IMRT) in which the radiation is directed from a donut-shaped machine that spirals around the body.

high-dose-rate (HDR) brachytherapy: a type of internal radiation in which the radioactive source is in place only for a few minutes and then removed. This may be repeated several times over a few days to weeks.

hyperfractionated radiation (hi-per-frack-shun-ate-ed): radiation schedule in which it is given in smaller doses and more than once a day, but the overall length of treatment is the same. (Compare to accelerated radiation.)

implant, radioactive: a small source or container of radioactive material placed in the body, either in or near a cancer. (See also brachytherapy.)

intensity modulated radiation therapy (IMRT) (in-ten-si-tee mod-you-late-ed): an advanced method of conformal radiation therapy in which the beams are aimed from many directions and the intensity (strength) of the beams is controlled by computers. This allows more radiation to reach the treatment area while reducing the radiation to healthy tissues. (See also conformal radiation therapy.)

internal radiation: a type of therapy in which a radioactive substance is implanted into or close to the area needing treatment. Also called brachytherapy.

interstitial radiation (in-ter-stih-shul): a type of internal radiation in which a radioactive source (implant) is put directly into the tissue (not in a body cavity).

intracavitary radiation (in-truh-kav-it-err-ee): a type of internal radiation in which a radioactive source (implant) is placed in a body cavity, such as the vagina, as opposed to directly into a tumor.

intraoperative radiation (in-truh-op-ruh-tiv): a type of external radiation therapy used to deliver a large dose of radiation to the tumor and surrounding tissue during surgery.

linear accelerator (lin-ee-er ak-sell-er-a-ter): a machine that creates high-energy radiation to treat cancers using electricity to form a beam of fast-moving subatomic particles. Also called mega-voltage (MeV) linear accelerator or a linac.

palliative care (pal-ee-uh-tiv): treatment intended to relieve symptoms caused by cancer, rather than to cure it. Palliative care can help people live more comfortably.

platelets (plate-uh-lets): special blood cell fragments that help stop bleeding.

port (also treatment field): the area of the body through which external beam radiation is directed to reach a tumor.

Radiation - Glossary

proton beam therapy: a form of external radiation that uses proton beams to kill cancer cells. Protons are parts of atoms that cause little damage to tissues they pass through but are very good at killing cells at the end of their path.

rad: short for "radiation absorbed dose"; an older term of measurement of the amount of radiation absorbed by the body (1 rad = 1 cGy). (See centigray.)

radiation: energy carried by waves or a stream of particles. Types of radiation used to treat cancer include x-ray, electron beam, alpha and beta particle, and gamma ray. Radioactive substances include forms of cobalt, radium, iridium, cesium, iodine, strontium, samarium, phosphorus, and palladium.

radiation oncologist: a doctor who specializes in using radiation to treat cancer.

radiation physicist: a person trained to ensure that the radiation machine delivers the right amount of radiation to the treatment area. This person works with the radiation oncologist and dosimetrist to design, plan, and calculate the proper dose for radiation treatment. (See dosimetrist.)

radiation therapist: a person with special training to work the equipment that delivers the radiation.

radiation therapy or **radiation treatment:** the use of high-energy rays or subatomic particles that penetrate the body to treat disease.

radiation therapy nurse: a registered nurse who has special training in oncology and radiation therapy.

radiologist: a doctor with special training in reading and interpreting diagnostic x-rays and scans and performing specialized x-ray procedures.

radiopharmaceuticals (ray-dee-o-farm-uh-SUIT-uh-kulls): radioactive substances that are taken by mouth or injected into the body. They collect in the area of the tumor and help stop its growth.

radio-resistance: the ability of cells to not be affected by radiation.

radio-sensitivity: how susceptible a cell, cancerous or healthy, is to radiation. Cells that divide frequently are especially radiosensitive and are more affected by radiation.

simulation: a process involving special x-ray pictures that is used to plan radiation treatment so that the area to be treated is precisely located and marked.

social worker: a mental health professional with a master's degree in social work (MSW). A social worker can help people manage medical, psychological, social, and educational needs.

stereotactic radiosurgery: a type of radiation treatment that gives a large dose of radiation to a small tumor area, usually in a single session. It is mostly used for brain tumors and other tumors inside the head. Though it is not surgery, it is able to focus the radiation on small areas. There are different types of equipment for this, such as the X-Knife□, CyberKnife□, Clinac□, and Gamma Knife□. Sometimes doctors give the radiation in many smaller treatments to deliver the same or slightly higher dose. This is sometimes called fractionated radiosurgery or stereotactic radiotherapy.

systemic radiation: uses radioactive materials such as iodine 131 and strontium 89 to kill cancer cells. The materials may be taken by mouth or injected into the body. (See radiopharmaceuticals.)

teletherapy (tell-uh-thair-up-ee): treatment in which the radiation source is at a distance from the body (external radiation).

treatment field (or port): the place on the body at which the radiation beam is aimed.

unsealed radiation: internal radiation therapy that is swallowed or given by injecting a radioactive substance into the bloodstream or a body cavity. This substance is not sealed in a container or implant.

Radiation

Today, I met my radiologist for the first time. He/she was

_____

_____

_____

_____

_____

_____

_____

_____

The advice that the radiologist gave me was

_____

_____

_____

_____

_____

_____

_____

_____

My questions about radiation

_____

_____

_____

_____

_____

_____

_____

_____

_____

_____

_____

_____

_____

_____

_____

_____

_____

_____

_____

_____

_____

_____

_____

Radiation - Getting Started

My first radiation treatment was today. It was

_____

_____

_____

_____

_____

_____

_____

_____

It felt like

_____

_____

_____

_____

I'm finished with a week of radiation already! Where did the time go?

_____

_____

_____

_____

_____

_____

I'm starting to get a little burned by the radiation. It's not terribly uncomfortable. (Hint - a silver nitrate prescription ointment is available to help with discomfort. They also have some great natural salves. Ask your radiologist).

_____

_____

_____

_____

_____

_____

_____

_____

_____

Second week of radiation is finished already!

_____

_____

_____

_____

_____

_____

_____

_____

Radiation - Crossing the Finish Line

It's been 3 weeks!

_____

_____

_____

_____

_____

_____

My last week of radiation!!!

_____

_____

_____

_____

_____

_____

_____

_____

_____

_____

_____

_____

_____

My thoughts about radiation:

_____

_____

_____

_____

_____

_____

_____

_____

_____

_____

_____

_____

_____

_____

_____

"When you get cancer, it's like really time to look
at what your life was and is,
and I decided that everything I've done so far
is not as important as what I'm going to do now."
Herbie Mann

Recovery

The Stages of Grief:

We go through many stages of grieving while
we are dealing with cancer. These stages are:
denial,
bargaining,
anger,
depression and, finally,
acceptance.
These stages don't happen in any particular order,
and they come and go.
Sometimes we can cycle through the stages many times
before reaching acceptance, and that's okay.
During the fight with cancer and our recovery,
we grieve over many different things,
each having it's own separate grieving process.
We may be in the acceptance stage of losing our hair,
but in the bargaining stage of dealing with bone pain.
It's all part of the process.

Don't give up!
We are all in this together.

Denial

Denial is the part where your mind won't let you believe that you have been diagnosed with a serious illness. It can take many forms. Some people believe they are sick, but don't think it's that serious. Others may just believe that they are going to die, no matter what treatment their doctor recommends. Regardless, denial affects us all. It's actually good for us! Remember that saying, that God will never give us more than we can actually handle? Denial can be a great friend!

Denial helped me by

_____

_____

_____

_____

_____

_____

_____

_____

_____

Am I still in denial?

_____

_____

_____

_____

_____

When I first heard the news, I reacted

_____

_____

_____

_____

_____

_____

I feel ready to face

_____

_____

_____

_____

_____

_____

Is it possible to be facing things one day and be in denial the next?

_____

_____

_____

_____

_____

_____

_____

Bargaining

Bargaining is when we begin to understand the reality of our situation and think that if we change something, the cancer will get better or the treatments will get easier. I did a lot of bargaining when I started chemo. I told myself, "the sicker I get, the sicker the cancer gets." It was a great mantra, and it got me through some rough nights. Bargaining helps us to feel more in control while we are afraid and spinning. Some people will donate money, completely change their lifestyles, or change their relationship patterns as a result of bargaining. It can be a very healthy thing to do, and it is a normal part of grieving.

I bargain by?

_____

_____

_____

Did any of those changes I made while bargaining affect my life in a positive way?

_____

_____

_____

Did any of these changes affect me in a negative way?

_____

_____

_____

Anger

Anger is the next stage. You can be grumpy, irritable, angry at your friends, healthy people, or even angry at God. Go ahead. Allow yourself to be angry. This sucks and you don't deserve it. God will still love you if you are angry. He understands that you need this emotion to give you energy.

"It will all be over soon"

From Rachael's Journal

April 24, 2006 - Ever since December, people have been saying to me, "Just think, this is the last big thing you have to go through. In another month, this will all be just a bad memory, and you'll be feeling great."

It is now April. I still feel awful. I have a giant hole in my back from where the incision from my reconstruction popped open and I have an infection in my right new boob. I've missed three weeks of classes, and I'm in unbearable pain if I go longer than five hours without a percoset. My pain meds have me so constipated, that I can't poop without getting blood everywhere. I am sore and I am angry and I am tired.

But no one seems to understand. Every time I complain about it, my friends and family all say, "But you beat cancer! This is nothing compared to that!" Why can't I make them understand that I am still fighting? That even though I am way ahead in points, the game isn't over yet? When I told people my surgery date and asked friends to pray for me, I got three emails back

93

Recovery

saying not to worry, I had a 14 hour surgery, this one should be nothing. It wasn't nothing to me.

It's hard too, that Eric wants to sugar coat everything when he passes news on to my friends and family. I want them to be concerned for me. I want them to know what I am going through, so that I don't feel so terribly alone. I want them to know how awful, painful, and messy this is. I don't like it when they say that they didn't know anything was wrong, because the last time they heard from us, everything was wonderful.

So much crap has happened lately. I am tired of being optimistic. I'm tired of talking about how wonderful this experience has been and how much I've learned. I want pity right now. I want people to say, "That poor girl" and to pray very hard that I make it through this without turning into a bitter, angry old cow. All I want right now is to get past this anger/depression and come out of it a more peaceful, loving person. Right now, I don't feel like being peaceful or loving. I just want to scream at everyone to leave me alone. I want them to stop calling and telling me to cheer up and be positive because it's almost over. It's not almost over. Even when I tell my friends and family that, they say I'm saying that because it's hard to see the end. I'm a realistic person. It's going to be at least two months before this hole heals up, at least two months before the tests are done on my heart, and I still need more reconstruction. It's not almost over! Optimism is great, but denial is annoying.

I want people to leave me alone right now. I don't want them to call me to tell me to cheer up. I don't want them to come over and talk to me for hours until I'm falling asleep in my chair. I don't want to have people telling me all the time that I need to look at the bright side of things. I want some chocolate. I want hugs. I want someone to volunteer to help Eric with the cleaning and the laundry and walking the dog. I want someone to call me and ask if they can do anything to help. I want Eric to get a rest. I don't want false encouragement, I want the same kind of support that I had when I had cancer! Now that it's gone, so has most of the support. Maybe I just need to start asking for help more. Eric is not going to ask, and he is looking so tired.

It's been four years since I was diagnosed. I've gone through chemo, a mastectomy, I've had my stomach muscles taken out and put in my chest only to have them fall off a few weeks later, I've had radiation, heart problems, a blood clot in my lung, a hernia, a giant hole in my back, and more surgeries than I can count. I've beaten cancer. So, now what?

I've tried to finish school and my brain doesn't work anymore. I can't concentrate on anything and I'm so impatient to get things accomplished that I keep forgetting to enjoy the ride.

I took up riding a year ago, bought a horse, and now I can't ride anymore. My upper body is so stiff, no matter how much stretching I do, that I can't look or feel relaxed on a horse. I can't bend at the waist to make jumping easier, and I can't flex. My balance is off and I just don't feel right. I've fallen off many times now and gotten hurt pretty badly.

Recovery

All I want is to be good at something! Now that the cancer is gone, I'm not good at anything again. I'm still shell-shocked and it's been a year and a half since I've had any surgeries or treatments. Everyone else is back to normal, but I'm not. I'm a fat, tired woman with no boobs, no muscle, no initiative and a terrible fear of achieving any of my goals. What is wrong with me?

I've been through the worst and lived through it. And I was good at it! When I had cancer, I was fighting for something. Everyday, I had a purpose, and this appreciation for life, no matter how sick or afraid I was. Now I am still in survival mode, but no one else is. When I had cancer, people cared about me. They cut me slack when I said stupid things, they laughed at my jokes, they were kind and friendly. Now I keep meeting people that treat me like I'm a loser. Now people act like they pity me because of what I've gone through, but they don't like me.

Eric tries to understand. He wants to help but he doesn't know how. I don't know how he can help, either. I want a job, but I don't want to do anything. I feel so entitled, like why should I have to do anything, I lived through cancer, and I STILL need a break. I'm not over it yet? How long will I have to get over it? When will I get over it? How long does it take other people to get over it?

I am angry because

_____

_____

_____

_____

_____

_____

_____

_____

I use my anger to give me the energy to

_____

_____

_____

_____

_____

What I've learned from my anger

_____

_____

_____

_____

_____

Recovery

This is a drawing out of my own journal expressing my anger. What does your anger look like?

Questions about anger

_____

_____

_____

_____

_____

_____

Thoughts about anger

_____

_____

_____

_____

_____

_____

_____

_____

_____

_____

_____

_____

_____

_____

_____

Depression

Depression is such a hard part of the grieving process. The world looks gray and dim and nothing seems fun anymore. Don't worry though, you are just as loveable when you are depressed. You are not going through this alone. People that you've never even met are praying for you and thinking good thoughts for you at this very moment! If you are having thoughts of suicide or hurting yourself, or even of just giving up, don't wait. Call someone right now.

"I don't feel like doing anything today, so maybe I won't.
Maybe I'll just nap instead." **Rachael**

Have you talked to your doctor about medication or seeing someone?

_____

_____

_____

_____

_____

_____

Is it okay for you to be depressed? If you happen to become afraid of your depression, who would you call?

_____

_____

_____

_____

_____

_____

"The positive effect of kindness on the immune system and on the increased production of serotonin in the brain has been proven in research studies. Serotonin is a naturally occurring substance in the body that makes us feel more comfortable, peaceful, and even blissful.

In fact, the role of most anti-depressants is to stimulate the production of serotonin chemically, helping to ease depression. Research has shown that a simple act of kindness directed toward another improves the functioning of the immune system and stimulates the production of serotonin in both the recipient of the kindness and the person extending the kindness. Even more amazing is that persons observing the act of kindness have similar beneficial results. Imagine this! Kindness extended, received, or observed beneficially impacts the physical health and feelings of everyone involved!" **Dr. Wayne Dyer**

Knowing this makes me feel

_____

_____

_____

_____

_____

_____

Recovery

Examine your depression. Is your body telling you that you need more time to rest?

_____

_____

What have you lost during this battle with cancer?

_____

_____

_____

_____

Now that you know what you have lost,
think about what you have gained - I'll help you...

Confidence. How do you handle making appointments, decisions, standing up for yourself now?

_____

_____

_____

Trust. Are you able to trust others more? Are you able to trust yourself?

_____

_____

_____

_____

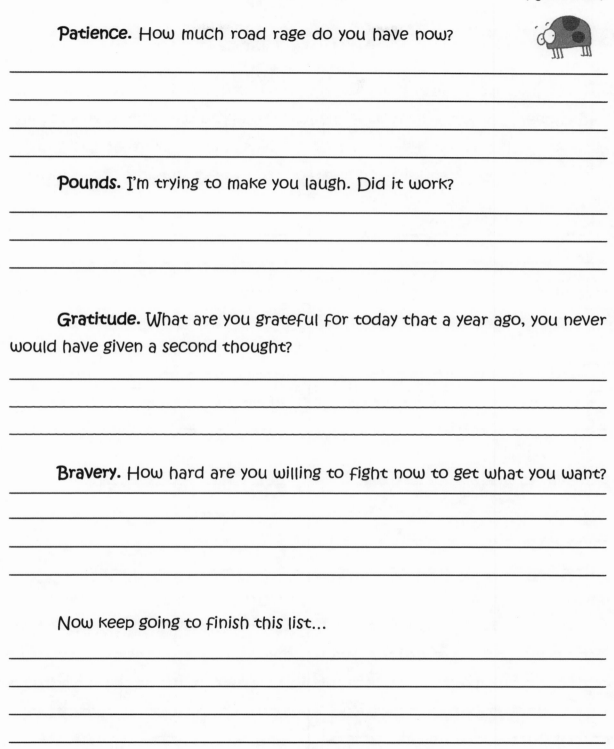

Patience. How much road rage do you have now?

_____

_____

_____

_____

Pounds. I'm trying to make you laugh. Did it work?

_____

_____

_____

Gratitude. What are you grateful for today that a year ago, you never would have given a second thought?

_____

_____

_____

Bravery. How hard are you willing to fight now to get what you want?

_____

_____

_____

_____

Now keep going to finish this list...

_____

_____

_____

_____

My Love List

A love list is a list of all the people that you had to call to tell that you had cancer. These are all people that love you. You can look at this list any time for a pick me up. Every time I read mine, I will know that there are a great many people that love and care for me. Cancer should not be hidden.

_____   _____

_____   _____

_____   _____

_____   _____

_____   _____

_____   _____

_____   _____

_____   _____

_____   _____

_____   _____

_____   _____

_____   _____

_____   _____

_____   _____

_____   _____

_____   _____

Acceptance

Acceptance. Do we ever reach this stage? Yes we do!

What have you begun to accept?

_____
_____
_____
_____
_____
_____

How do you know?

_____
_____
_____

How has acceptance changed you?

_____
_____
_____
_____
_____
_____
_____
_____

Recovery

Thoughts on acceptance

_____
_____
_____
_____
_____
_____
_____
_____
_____
_____

Questions about acceptance

_____
_____
_____
_____
_____
_____
_____
_____

I still have some wounds that haven't healed...

My doctor says

_____
_____
_____
_____
_____
_____
_____
_____

I want them to heal

_____
_____
_____
_____
_____
_____
_____
_____
_____
_____
_____
_____

Recovery

Before I got sick, my biggest dream was

_____

_____

_____

_____

_____

_____

_____

_____

_____

Now my biggest dream is

_____

_____

_____

_____

_____

_____

_____

"Drag your thoughts away from your troubles...
by the ears, by the heels,
or any other way you can manage it."
Mark Twain

What I miss the most about being healthy is

_____

_____

_____

_____

_____

_____

_____

_____

_____

_____

When I'm healthy again, the first thing I'm going to do is

_____

_____

_____

_____

_____

_____

_____

_____

_____

Recovery

I have so many scars now

_____

_____

_____

_____

_____

_____

_____

_____

_____

I know that they will fade, but I

_____

_____

_____

_____

_____

_____

_____

_____

_____

_____

Pets are nice to have around when I don't feel well. This is how they comfort me

_____

_____

_____

_____

_____

_____

_____

_____

_____

Sometimes they are also a pain in the butt. They drive me crazy when

_____

_____

_____

_____

_____

_____

How is this a reminder of what love really is?

_____

_____

_____

Recovery

List the types of Nurses that you have seen

_____

_____

_____

_____

_____

_____

_____

The types of Doctors (aren't specialists weird?)

_____

_____

_____

_____

_____

_____

A common saying among cancer patients is "I can be bitter or I can be better." What does this saying mean? How do you feel about it? How do you want cancer to change you?

_____

_____

_____

_____

_____

How has cancer changed you already?

_____

_____

_____

_____

_____

_____

_____

_____

I am afraid of dying. What is it about death that scares me?

_____

_____

_____

_____

_____

_____

_____

_____

_____

_____

Recovery

I am very happy today and I feel so good!

_____

_____

_____

_____

_____

_____

_____

_____

_____

_____

_____

_____

_____

_____

_____

_____

"Difficult times have helped me to understand
better than before how infinitely rich and beautiful life is
in every way and that so many things that one goes worrying
about are of no importance whatsoever."
Isak Dineses

Odds and Ends

From Rachael's Journal: Boredom

10/16/2005 - I have done it. I am now the crazy lady of the neighborhood. I had blown past the lady in the muumuu that sits in her yard and screams all day and nite for Fred. I have passed up the old lady with the perpetual-diarrhea-dog that comes outside with a ruler every afternoon to measure if anyone has parked too close to her handicap space. No, I am the ruler of them all. I stand in the front yard everyday peering over the fence, wearing my pajamas, socks and a bathrobe. The dog stands next to me. Together, we look up and down the street. Then we look around the yard at all the spots where the grass used to grow. In the afternoons, when I hear kids walking down the sidewalk in front of our house, the dog and I fight to get to the window first to look out. Sometimes, plants are knocked over in the struggle. I am bored, hopelessly bored. I have no life. My paints are dried out, and I am out of canvas. My house is a mess. Old magazines and copies of insurance claims cover every space that used to be open. Stacks of papers are everywhere. This is my fault. Eric cleans, but the clutter just follows me back downstairs. He knows I know it's my fault. He says nothing and cleans. I am slowly disappearing into a 20 year old easy chair. The outline of my body is clearly visible in the upholstery of the chair when I stand up. What do I do now? My friends and family have heart attacks if I take the dog for a walk, I am still too out of it to drive. I am very weak, so what would I do if I drove somewhere? Turn around and drive back? I am turning into a couch potato, but I watch the TV without turning it on. I just stare at it. I have read every book in my house at least 3 times, including the Bible. I surf the internet for pictures of horses for sale, just to keep my hopes up. I am going crazy. I need to get out.

Write your own boredom story...

_____

_____

_____

_____

_____

_____

_____

_____

_____

_____

_____

_____

_____

_____

_____

_____

_____

_____

_____

"Puttering is really a time to be alone,
to dream and to get in touch with yourself....
To putter is to discover."
Alexandra Stoddard

Odds and Ends

Insomnia

You would think that after all this, I'd be able to sleep!

_____

_____

_____

_____

_____

_____

_____

_____

_____

_____

_____

_____

_____

_____

_____

_____

_____

_____

_____

I want

_____
_____
_____
_____
_____
_____
_____

I need

_____
_____
_____
_____
_____
_____
_____

I feel

_____
_____
_____
_____
_____
_____
_____

Odds and Ends

My family and friends are the greatest! They

_____

_____

_____

_____

_____

_____

_____

_____

_____

Sometimes, however, I need to set some boundaries for them in a kind and loving way. How can I do this?

_____

_____

_____

_____

_____

_____

_____

_____

Money is tight right now. I feel

_____

_____

_____

_____

_____

_____

I can help to budget by

_____

_____

_____

_____

_____

_____

_____

_____

_____

_____

_____

_____

Odds and Ends

There are _____ fish tanks in my doctors office.

Have a conversation with the person that takes care of the tank and write about it.

_____

_____

_____

_____

_____

_____

_____

_____

_____

_____

_____

_____

_____

_____

_____

_____

_____

_____

Insecurity

Entry from Rachael's Journal

4-15-2006 - Does the doctor ever really say, "Congratulations, you're cured!" Does that big day ever come? I have been getting tons of emails asking when I know that the cancer is gone and that everything is great. I don't know. I wonder if they ever say? I'm going to ask for a PET scan, and then I can tell everyone myself!

_____

_____

_____

_____

_____

_____

_____

_____

_____

_____

_____

_____

_____

_____

_____

STDS

    "Sieze the Day Syndrome" happens when you start to feel better! People have been telling you for months to "live every day like it's your last," and now that you are feeling better, you want to! It's not very realistic though, is it? Please no cliff-diving!

_____

_____

_____

_____

_____

_____

_____

_____

_____

_____

_____

_____

_____

_____

_____

_____

_____

_____

_____

Ask a nurse what her favorite hobby is and write about your conversation

_____

_____

_____

_____

_____

_____

_____

_____

_____

_____

_____

_____

Ask a nurse how many children she has and write about your conversation

_____

_____

_____

_____

Odds and Ends

How do you feel about these quotes?

"Cancer can make me bitter, or it can make me better." *Unknown*

_____

_____

_____

_____

_____

_____

_____

_____

"The scars that you acquire while excercising courage
will never make you feel inferior." **D.A.Battista**

_____

_____

_____

_____

_____

_____

_____

Below are 31 Tools That I Discovered During my Journey That I Hope Will Make Yours a Little Easier!

1. **Use your emotions to give you adrenalin.** If you are angry, use it to express how you feel and to give you the energy to do something nice for yourself, like make a milkshake, take a short easy walk, or write in your journal. This will make you feel more productive, and give you a little something to do to expend your nervous energy. Remember-most of the agitation is from steroids and other meds-you are NOT going crazy!

2. **Tell everyone that you want to tell.** You will be surprised at how much support you receive. The more people that you talk to, the more prayers that will be said, and the more supported you will feel. It will make you feel much safer. It's also great practice for stress reduction during all of life's challenges. Sharing with others helps to calm us, reduce our stress, and make friends.

3. **Don't overdo it!** Schedule time for naps! After one or two chemos, your body will begin to tell you that you need rest *before* you become fatigued. Pay attention to feelings of discomfort, restlessness, or inability to concentrate (more so than your "normal" chemo-brain). Sometimes your body will tell you it needs rest by sending you abnormal thoughts. If you are doing something, and have a thought like, "what if I was to fall down right now," or, "what if I become too tired to finish this project," STOP! Your body is telling you that such a situation is likely if you don't rest. Thoughts like that often happen to people about 20 to 30 minutes before a fatigue crash.

4. **If friends or family are starting to smother, give them a job!** Tell them that you appreciate their enthusiasm, and you could really use help with the laundry, or scrubbing toilets (anyone that does this for you will become your new hero. Not only is it a great way to get some chores done around your house but it also gives your friends and family a way to stop feeling helpless for a little while. Once they have completed a task for you, they are much more likely to let you nap!

5. **Drink LOTS of water!** Especially the few days before and after chemotherapy. Some chemo treatments can cause kidney, liver and/or bladder damage, so staying properly hydrated is a must. My oncologist recommended drinking sixty-four ounces of water a day during Adriamycin®/Cytoxan® treatments.

6. **Honor your emotions!** Being angry, frustrated, or sad has nothing to do with your positive outlook. You WILL bounce back after a few days. Remember, chemo and steroids will cause you to be emotional as well. The sooner (and louder) you express your emotions, the sooner you will feel back to normal. Just remember to be kind- your loved ones are angry and frustrated too.

7. **Inform your family/friends that you will be emotional**, both from the meds, and because you have a LOT of grieving to do. That way, if something is said rashly, it is much easier to apologize for it later.

8. **Ask your oncologist** what foods will help you to boost your blood count and keep you healthy. If they do not recommend anything, or just

recommend taking a vitamin, ask for websites or names of dieticians that they recommend you go to for help. Good nutrition makes a huge difference in how quickly your body bounces back from chemo. Be sure to okay ANY diet changes with your oncologist. Some vitamins and supplements interact adversely with chemo and other medications. Visit our website at: http://wheresmyboob.com for more information.

9. **Let the phone ring** if you don't want to talk, or ask a loved one to run interference for you. Let them answer the phone and say that you are unable to talk. Allow yourself to decide what makes you feel better and act accordingly.

10. **Make a list** of the things you CAN control vs. the things that you can't when you are afraid or stressed. You will be surprised at what you see.

11. **Keep a journal**. It doesn't have to be a diary. Use markers, crayons, draw your emotions if you don't feel like a writer. Or just color the pages. Let it be a reflection of how you feel at that moment. It will become a cherished possession and an invaluable way to help you chart your progress.

12. **Keep all of your cards** in a special box or folder, because you will receive lots of them! When you are feeling down, read through them. Instant pick-me-up!

13. **Contact the American Cancer Society**. They have 24 hour telephone counseling, offer makeup tips, support group information, healthy recipes, and other advice.

14. **Get a massage** or healing touch the day before each chemo. If expense is a problem, the ACS can get you in touch with agencies that will come to your home and do it for free! It makes a HUGE difference in how you feel the next few days.

15. **Don't expect your chemo side effects to follow a schedule**. They change in frequency and intensity from treatment to treatment.

16. **Be your own best advocate**. As soon as you and your oncologist set a plan for your treatment, ask him/her for the names and dosage of the medicines he plans to use, and a list of their side effects *before* the day you come into the office for treatment. *It helps to know about the potential side effects a few days before your first treatment*, so that you have time to ask questions about controlling them.

17. **Schedule your chemos at the beginning of the week**, like Monday, Tuesday, or Wednesday. If you schedule them late in the week, it will be very difficult to contact your doctor and pharmacy over the weekend, should uncomfortable side effects occur that you need treated right away. Emergency room doctors are not usually as well informed about treating side effects, and will usually just refer you back to your oncologist anyway.

18. **Don't hesitate to call your doctor at any time** if your side effects are painful or bothersome. It is their job to help you get through this ordeal, and keeping you comfortable is a huge part of that job.

19. **DO NOT exercise by yourself** if you suffer from fatigue or pain after surgery or treatments. Even during a light walk, your energy can get away from you. Ask a friend to go with you. If this is not possible, at least take a cell phone with you, and notify someone of where you will be before you leave the house.

20. **Email and Facebook updates** are a great way to keep everyone informed without having to make lots of phone calls. It also is helpful to update people when you are on the upswing from treatment. Conversations are less tiring and you will feel more upbeat during this time.

21. **Set up a phone tree by** e-mailing or calling your friends and family before you start treatment, and asking each of them to call just one or two specific people on your list. This way, you or a loved one can make one call to the first person on your phone tree with updates and from there, they call their list and they call their list and so on.

22. **Cut maxi pads and diapers** in half for use as substitutes for non-sterile gauze padding. They are cheaper and much more absorbent! They are also easier to shape and stuff into bras. If using to dress a wound, BE SURE to put a piece of sterile gauze or dressing between the wound and the absorbent material to reduce the risk of infection. Always check with your surgeon before making any changes to your wound care.

23. **Listen to books on CD** during chemo treatments or while you are sitting in the doctor's office waiting for your appointment. Books on CD

or iPod are also great for when you just want to hear a person's voice in the background.

24. **Use satin or sateen sheets and pillow cases** if your skin gets sensitive. They are cooler and softer and they also make it easier to slide out of bed. (I recommend the sateen sheets rather than satin, they are more cottony and less likely to slide off the bed.

25. **Keep butterscotch disks or Jolly ranchers** with you during chemo treatment time – some of the medicines you will be taking will leave a bad taste in your mouth as they are administered.

26. **Ask your oncologist and surgeons about a condition called "lymphedema"** before you have surgery.

27. **Take a cell phone with you.** You never know when you may need to call a friend or family member because you need help. The need might arise for help in some way.

28. **Take your meds with you to emergency room visits.** If you are admitted to the hospital, it can take several hours or even days for the nurses to contact your physician for prescription drug approval. Be sure to let the doctors and nurses know that you are taking them to avoid mistakes!

29. **Take hand sanitizer with you to the emergency** room and a surgical mask if you have it. Emergency rooms are cesspools for germs, especially the restrooms.

30. **Call your oncologist** if you feel that an emergency room doctor is unconcerned about you or if something doesn't feel right. Trust me, your oncologist and his staff will work hard to protect you!

31. **There is always hope.** You will find it in some very strange and unlikely places, as well as with your loved ones. People that you have never even met are hoping (pulling) for you right now. You are never alone, even if it feels that way.

"It is good to have an end to journey towards;

but it is the journey that matters in the end."

Ursula K. LeGuin

Resources

My Vital Signs Record

Date	Blood Pressure	Iron-hemoglobin	WBC	Platelets	Weight

Resources

Recommended Reading

"Love Medicine and Miracles", Dr. Bernie Siegel,

"Transformation Soup", SARK,

"Why I wore Lipstick to My Mastectomy", Geralyn Lucas (great movie as well!),

"Lessons from a Bald Chick", Mary Beth Hall.

Recommended Websites

For more links and all kinds of helpful information, visit our website at:

http://wheresmyboob.com

My Thoughts are Free to Fly

My thoughts are Free to Fly

I encourage you to use the pages that follow to explore your feelings about
this journey on paper, so you can leave them here and move forward
with the next chapter of your life!

Remember that what you have just been through
required an extraordinary amount of courage and focus,
so pat yourself on the back for forging ahead
and getting through it!

_____

_____

_____

_____

_____

_____

_____

_____

_____

_____

_____

_____

_____

_____

_____

My thoughts are Free to Fly

Here are a few things that I invite you to write about in the pages that follow so that you get the most out of this journey!

» What did you learn about yourself during this experience?

» What did you learn about those family and friends closest to you during this experience?

» Did you ever think you could get through something as tough as this BEFORE you were diagnosed?

» What do you admire most about yourself now?

» Have you learned to be more tolerant of others through this experience and if you did, have you learned to be more tolerant of your own limitations as well?

» Have you made new friends and how important are they to you?

» How has this experience changed what was important to you in your life?

What else do you want to share on these pages about your personal journey?

_____

_____

_____

_____

_____

_____

_____

_____

_____

_____

_____

_____

_____

_____

_____

_____

_____

_____

_____

_____

_____

_____

_____

_____

_____

_____

_____

_____

_____

My thoughts are Free to Fly

My thoughts are Free to Fly

Order Page

To order on-line, visit wheresmyboob.com.
We accept all major credit cards through our secure PayPal account. *You can now process your credit card through PayPal whether you have an account with them or not!*

If you prefer to mail your order to us, please fill out the form below and mail it to the address provided.

Quantity		Price	Total
_____	The Gown Opens in the Front,	$19.95	_____
_____	Personal Journal for Cancer Patients,	$12.99	_____
_____	The Caregiver's Journal,	$12.99	_____

Shipping & Handling   ($3.00 per book)   _____

Total   _____

Shipping Information:

Name: _____

Ship To Address: _____

City: _____

State/Zip: _____

Home Phone: _____

Select your payment method: _____ check, _____ credit card

Credit Card #: _____

Exp. Date: _____

Name on the Card: _____

Mail your order with your payment to:

The Gown Opens in the Front
PO Box 122322
Covington, KY 41012-2322

144

Made in the USA
Charleston, SC
09 March 2010